THE  TIMES

THE BEST OF

QUEEN'S COUNSEL

THE TIMES
THE BEST OF
QUEEN'S COUNSEL

STEUART AND FRANCIS

TIMES BOOKS
London

Published by
Times Books
HarperCollins*Publishers*
77-85 Fulham Palace Road
Hammersmith
London W6 8JB

First published in 1999 by Times Books

Printed and bound in Great Britain by The Bath Press Limited

British Library Cataloguing in Publication Data
A catalogue record for this book is available from the British Library

The Times is a registered trademark of Times Newspapers Limited, a subsidiary of News International plc.

ISBN 0-7230-1071-4

The Authors

Alex Steuart Williams is a former barrister turned cartoonist and feature film animator. He is currently working at Dreamworks studios in Los Angeles in the forthcoming _Road to El Dorado_. His film credits include _Who Framed Roger Rabbit?_, _The Lion King_, _Pocahontas_ and _The Iron Giant_. His cartoons have been published in _The Times_ and _Tatler_.

Graham Francis Defries is a solicitor with the City law firm Bird & Bird. Prior to becoming a lawyer, he had a range of jobs including a parliamentary research assistant for a Member of Parliament and a music promoter. In addition to books of Queen's Counsel cartoons, he has contributed to _Internet Law and Regulation_, published by FT Law & Tax. He is married with a young son and daughter and lives in London.

Foreword

"I have written out my judgement, 300 pages of it. I have assessed all the witnesses, decided all the points of rule and come to a just verdict."

It was Monday morning and a packed court was waiting for the judge to give his decision after a lengthy case. "Unfortunately I have left it all in my cottage in Wales and I can't get it up here before tomorrow morning. So we'll have to adjourn until then."

"Fax it up, my lord," said a helpful barrister. "Yes," the judge replied ruefully, "It does rather."

This is the archetypal legal joke. It sets up self-importance, pomposity and the voice of authority and pricks them so that the awe-inspiring judge appears as a fallible, indeed a rather ridiculous, human being. This is what Steuart and Francis's excellent legal strip does so brilliantly.

When I became a barrister, I quickly discovered how easy it is to bear other people's worries with great courage, and solve other people's problems with no trouble at all. What we all have to remember is that lawyers and judges, pontificating about the importance of marriage and standards of honesty, are no doubt sleeping with their pupils and presenting blurred accounts to the tax inspector. Comedy flourishes when men and women with high pretensions slide on moral banana skins. This happens most satisfactorily in law courts, and Steuart and Francis take glorious advantage of it.

Sir John Mortimer

"*I was only ruined but twice – once when
I lost a lawsuit and once when I won one*"

Voltaire

8

9

13

WHAT DO YOU MAKE OF THAT CHAP FARQUAR, EDWARD?

THE QC AT FOUNTAIN BUILDING? NEVER LIKED HIM, I'M AFRAID.

—ARROGANT, AND NOT VERY BRIGHT EITHER. WHY DO YOU ASK?

APPARENTLY HE'S GONE GA-GA.—FORCED INTO EARLY RETIREMENT.

OH DEAR. POOR FELLOW.

YES. A SAD END TO HIS CAREER.

HIGH COURT JUDGE?

—APPOINTED LAST WEEK.

27

28

I'M AFRAID I HAVE NO TIME FOR THE PUBLICITY-SEEKING LAWYERS INVOLVED IN THE O.J. SIMPSON TRIAL.

THE MEDIA LAVISH ATTENTION ON THEM OUT OF ALL PROPORTION TO THEIR SKILLS AS ADVOCATES.

THE TV NETWORKS PAY CELEBRITY ATTORNEYS ABSURD SUMS TO APPEAR AS COMMENTATORS.

THE WHOLE TRIAL IS NOTHING BUT A MEDIA CIRCUS.

31

AND WHEN YOUR HONOUR HAS FINISHED TAKING OUT THE RUBBISH HE CAN WASH THE DISHES

LADIES AND GENTLEMEN, THE INDEPENDENCE OF THE JUDICIARY IS THE VERY CORNERSTONE OF ENGLISH LIBERTY.

AS A RECORDER, I JUDGE WITHOUT REGARD TO POLITICAL PRESSURE OR PUBLIC OPINION.

WHEN I PASS SENTENCE, NO POLITICIAN, NO NEWS-PAPER, NO PRESSURE GROUP AFFECTS MY JUDGMENT.

DADDY, IF YOU SEND THAT POOR MAN TO PRISON I'LL NEVER SPEAK TO YOU AGAIN!

NOR ME.

OH, ALL RIGHT THEN. COMMUNITY SERVICE IT IS.

36

WHEN LAWYERS WIN

... AND WHEN THEY LOSE

LEGAL OLYMPICS

SYNCHRONISED BILLING

CROSS-COUNTRY AMBULANCE DASH

PARTNERSHIP PROMOTION WRESTLE

LONG DISTANCE RUN UP EXPENSE ACCOUNT

WHAT KIND OF LAW PRACTICE IS RIGHT FOR YOU?

WE'VE GOT A CAST-IRON ALIBI THIS TIME, MR LONG-WIND. THE DEFENDANT WAS AT THE BETTING SHOP WHEN THE ROBBERY TOOK PLACE — AND HIS BOOKIE WILL BE A WITNESS.

I DON'T THINK THE JURY WILL LIKE THE BETTING SHOP MUCH, RICHARD.

I SUPPOSE YOU'RE RIGHT.

TAP TAP

WHISPER...

ER... ACTUALLY HE WAS LOOKING AFTER HIS MOTHER-IN-LAW ALL EVENING, AND SHE'LL BE A WITNESS INSTEAD.

EXCELLENT

47

PLEASE TELL THE COURT, IN YOUR OWN WORDS, WHAT HAPPENED ON THE NIGHT OF THE ROBBERY.

ER... CAN'T I USE MY LAWYER'S WORDS INSTEAD?

49

53

57

FAMILY LAW

LEGAL BILLINGS

MR "I'LL BILL WHAT I'M WORTH"

> I'M WORTH 10 ORDINARY LAWYERS, SO I'LL BILL 10 HOURS FOR EVERY HOUR I WORK

MISS "SOCIAL JUSTICE"

> LET'S SEE ... GREENPEACE, ½ TIME ... BIG OIL Co, DOUBLE TIME...

THE "REVENGE BILLER"

> ANOTHER EVENING RUINED! THIS TAKEOVER IS DESTROYING MY SOCIAL LIFE! MEGACORP: 60 HOURS

THE HONEST BILLER

> SORRY OLD CHAP—YOU'RE JUST NOT BILLING ENOUGH HOURS

P45

"I DON'T UNDERSTAND HOW WE COULD LOSE!
WE HAD THE BEST WITNESSES MONEY COULD BUY!"

LAWYER'S PSYCHIATRIC DISORDERS

PARTNER PHOBIA

FEAR OF MEETING A PARTNER IN AN UNCOMFORTABLE ENVIRONMENT

BUSY, CRAWLEY?

ER...

WG

SELF–DELUSION SYNDROME

FASCINATING CASE I'M WORKING ON. BOUND TO BE IN THE LAW REPORTS.

LIKEWISE

POST ALL-NIGHTER STRESS DISORDER

NOW THAT YOU'VE COMPLETED THE MEGABANK TAKEOVER, HERE ARE SOME OTHER FILES FOR YOUR ATTENTION

OK

ANAL RETENTIVENESS

I FOUND ANOTHER TYPO, HELENA.

BUT THAT'S MY WEEKEND SHOPPING LIST, SIR GEOFFREY

74

81

82

A GUIDE TO LEGAL DRAFTING

NEVER CHOOSE SIMPLE WORDS WHERE COMPLEX ONES WILL ~~DO~~ PROVE REASONABLY PRACTICABLE

NEVER USE ONE DOUBLE NEGATIVE WHERE NO TRIPLE NEGATIVE WILL NOT PROVE UNECESSARY.

MAKE FREE USE OF (a) SUB-PARAGRAPHS, and (b) (i) SUB-SUB-PARAGRAPHS and (ii) SCHEDULES

(SEE ATTACHED SCHEDULE).

THE ONLY DOCUMENT YOUR CLIENT SHOULD BE ABLE TO UNDERSTAND IS YOUR BILL.

84

MORE
LEGAL BILLINGS

THE "GREEDY BILLER"

SINCE YOU'RE ALL WORKING ON MY CASE I'M RE-ALLOCATING YOUR BILLABLE HOURS TO ME

MR "LEGAL RESEARCH"

FOUND THAT CASE YET, CRAWLEY?

NOT YET, EDWARD

XXX.com

THE "SOLE PRACTITIONER" BILLER

CLIENT'S WILL — 1 HOUR

WALKING CLIENT'S DOG — 1 HOUR

HOLDING CLIENT'S HAND — 1 HOUR

MR "REVIEWING AND CONSIDERING CASE — ½ HOUR"

CONTINGENCY FEES EXPLAINED